G000152773

The Grea Irish Women Colouring Book

Written & Illustrated by Diana Matos Gagic

**First published in 2020 by
Crafty Birdie Designs**

Text copyright © Diana Gagic, 2020
Illustrations copyright © Diana Gagic, 2020

Design for print by
Fullstop Studio

Edited by
Emma Turner

Created in Yorkshire

The moral right of Diana Gagic to be identified as the author and illustrator
of this work has been asserted in accordance with Sections 77 and 78
of the Copyright, Designs and Patents Act 1988.

All rights reserved.
No part of this book may be reproduced, transmitted or stored in any form
or by any means, graphic, electronic or mechanical, including photocopying, taping
and recording, without prior written permission from the publisher.

email: dgagic.dg@gmail.com
www.etsy.com/uk/shop/CraftyBirdieDesigns

Printed in England

ISBN 978-1-9160072-6-0

This book has been made with responsibly sourced uncoated paper
(and love) and is suitable for colouring in using pens, pencils or crayons
of your choosing... so feel free to be as creative as you like!

About the Author / Illustrator

Diana has lived for many years in the beautiful, historic Yorkshire village of Haworth, home to the famous Brontë family during the Victorian era. Like the Brontës, Diana loved to draw and create as a young girl and remains passionate about the arts, nature, truth and equality. This hand-illustrated book evolved from a desire to help keep alive the memory of some of Ireland's great, inspirational women; aiming to honour the brave ladies who battled the odds to stand up for what they believed in and in doing so helped to encourage new generations to aim for their dreams and be true to themselves.

Irish Women

Our history books are filled with stories of the great deeds of politicians, writers, artists, scientists and innovators. They are brave and fearless — and almost all men. Let us not forget the remarkable women whose work also helped to transform the lives of others, and in many cases, the course of history. This book aims to highlight and celebrate some of Ireland's epic female pioneers from the past and present, a diverse bunch who share the legacy of making positive contributions to society as we know it, helping to encourage new generations of brave and fearless women!

Margaret Ann Bulkley

(c. 1789 - 1865)

Margaret Bulkley was born in Cork, Republic of Ireland in 1789. At that time a university education was not open to women so as a clever ploy to enter, Margaret pretended to be a man and adopted the pseudonym of James Barry. In 1813 'Barry' successfully passed the examination of the Royal College of Surgeons of England and went on to become a high ranking military surgeon in the British Army. She brought about many improvements to public health through better sanitation and nutrition, as well as having performed one of the first caesarean-sections in which both mother and baby survived. Margaret's unusual life provides us with a glimpse into what women might have achieved throughout history had gender expectations and education been fairer. Her well-kept secret was only revealed after her death, when her instructions that she be buried without an inspection of her body were ignored!

Mary Harris Jones
(c. 1837 - 1930)

Mary Harris was born in Cork in 1837. She then moved to North America where she grew up to become a teacher and a seamstress. She suffered immense tragedy in her personal life, when in 1867, her husband and their four children all died during a yellow fever epidemic. Further misfortune struck when the Great Chicago Fire of 1871 destroyed her dress shop. Hardship appeared to energise her to improve the lives of her fellow working class and she went on to become a powerful trade unionist and activist described as "the most dangerous woman in America" and now remembered by the name 'Mother Jones'. Her trademark being peaceful mass action, she organised the 1903 crusade against child labour, leading a children's march from Philadelphia to New York. In 1915, she testified against the abuse of corporate power by Rockefeller interests and at the age of 82, was arrested for defending freedom of speech and the right to union representation during a Pennsylvania steelworkers' strike. In 1984, she was inducted into the U.S. National Women's Hall of Fame.

Margaret Elizabeth Cousins
(1878 - 1954)

Margaret 'Gretta' Cousins was born in Boyle, County Roscommon. She was a strong-willed girl about whom her headmistress had warned "should not be so independent" – advice she thankfully went on to ignore! She graduated from the Royal University of Ireland in 1902 and became a music teacher who refused to give up her job after marriage as was expected at the time. Passionate about women's rights, she joined the Irish Women's Suffrage Society and in 1908 went on to co-found the Irish Women's Franchise League with Hanna Sheehy-Skeffington. Her strong beliefs led to brief imprisonments for taking part in public protests over the decision to deny women the right to vote. She and her husband then moved to India in 1915 where she continued to campaign for women's rights, organising the first All-India and All-Asia women's conferences in 1927. She is the author of three books on women's rights in India and her campaigns led to the eventual introduction of compulsory education for girls in Madras in 1932. In the same year, her brave support of Gandhi's free-speech campaign landed her a further spell behind bars. When India gained independence in 1947, following 200 years of British rule, Gretta's positive contributions were finally recognised and she was awarded 5,000 rupees for her services to the Indian state.

Mary, Lady Heath
(1896 - 1939)

Mary was baptised as Sophie Peirce-Evans in Knockaderry, County Limerick, but after a tragic start in life was renamed and brought up by her secondary relatives. She went on to become a multi record-breaking aviator, athlete, women's rights campaigner and one of the most famous women in the world in the mid-1920s. In 1925, as a founding member of the Women's Amateur Athletic Association, she undertook her maiden solo flight to Prague to address the Olympic Congress where she campaigned to have women's athletics accepted at the Olympic Games. Mary was Britain's first women's javelin champion and also set a world record for the high jump. She was the first person, male or female, to fly solo across Africa from South Africa to London – a perilous 10,000 miles in unbearable heat in an open-air cockpit! She was also the first woman to parachute from an aeroplane and the first to undertake a mechanic's qualification in the U.S. To top it all, this high flyer then took on the male establishment to win her licence to become the first female commercial pilot in the U.K.

Mainie Jellett
(1897 - 1944)

Mary Harriet 'Mainie' Jellett was born in Dublin. As a young girl she received painting lessons from various female tutors, then studied at the Metropolitan School of Art in Dublin, the Westminster Technical Institute in London and later trained in France. Mainie went on to become one of the most significant Irish artists of the 20th century and is widely credited with introducing modernism to Ireland when her abstract paintings were first exhibited at the Society of Dublin Painters Group Show in 1923. Her works were initially ridiculed by Irish art critics as "a dangerous source of foreign notions" but she fearlessly persevered in developing her own unique hybrid style, combining cubism, Celtic design and religious art. With a growing acceptance for her art and the work of other modern artists, she went on to become a founding member of the Abstraction-Création group which led the European Abstract Movement in the 1930s. She said "The art of a nation is one of the ultimate facts by which its spiritual health is judged and appraised by posterity." Mainie's legacy as a pioneering champion of modern art maintains her place as one of the most important and influential figures in Irish art history.

Dame Ninette de Valois
(1898 - 2001)

Edris Stannus was born into a comfortable life in County Wicklow and moved to England when young. She went on to become widely regarded as one of the most influential figures in the history of ballet and as the "godmother" of English and Irish ballet. A classical ballerina, teacher and choreographer, she was better known by her stage name, Ninette de Valois. In 1923, de Valois joined the Ballets Russes where she developed her ambition to start her own company and in 1927 she opened the Academy of Choreographic Art, Kensington and the Abbey Theatre School of Ballet, Dublin, both early predecessors of the Royal Ballet School. In her later years she continued to work with the Royal Ballet Benevolent Fund to support retired dancers and, with concern for their financial stability, she raised the issue of salaries and pension provision. She was appointed Dame in 1951, received an Order of Merit in 1992 and was awarded honorary doctorates from several British universities.

Kay McNulty Antonelli
(1921 - 2006)

Kathleen 'Kay' McNulty Mauchly Antonelli was born in County Donegal in Ulster. On the night of her birth her father was arrested and imprisoned for two years, accused of being a member of the IRA. Following his release the family emigrated to the U.S. where Kathleen proved to be a brilliant mathematician and went on to become one of the original 'human-computer' programmers of the first ever electronic computer, ENIAC. Initially her top secret work was part of the war effort and involved laboriously calculating trajectories for missile fire. She later worked on the software design for newer computers including the BINAC and UNIVAC I. The contributions of Kathleen and her fellow female programmers to the world of computer science were unacknowledged in official histories of the war and the development of computers for many years. However, their vital role was finally recognised in 1997 when the original ENIAC programmers were inducted into the Women in Technology International Hall of Fame.

Rosemary Smith
(b. 1937)

Rosemary Smith was born in Dublin. Impeccably glamorous, she was initially dismissed as a 'dolly bird' when she first started rally car racing but she went on to turn heads in a notable way when she became an Irish racing legend in the male-dominated world of motorsport. Rallies take place on public or private roads with modified or specially built road-legal cars and Rosemary became a female pioneer when she broke through the gender barrier to compete in and win some of the most iconic motorsport rallies all around the world. In 1965, in a Hillman Imp, Rosemary won the Dutch Tulip Rally outright, beating all the male drivers to the finish. She participated in the legendary Monte Carlo rally on numerous occasions, the London to Sydney in 1968, the World Cup London to Mexico in 1970 and the East African Safari Rally in the 1970s. Rosemary remains a great ambassador for motorsport and women's place in it and even holds the record for the oldest-ever person to drive a Formula 1 car at the age of 79!

Mary Robinson
(b. 1944)

Mary Therese Winifred Bourke was born in Ballina, County Mayo. She studied law at Trinity College, Dublin and graduated to become a well-respected barrister and Independent/Labour party politician who went on to be elected as the first female President of Ireland in 1990. During her time in office she advocated for the right to the legal availability of contraception, a removal of the requirement that married women resign from the civil service, the right for women to sit on juries and is most noted for passing two important bills into law; legalisation of contraception and decriminalising homosexuality. She resigned as President in 1997 to take up an equally prestigious role serving as the United Nations High Commissioner for Human Rights. Mary continues to work with the world's top leaders on various environmental and humanitarian issues and set up The Mary Robinson Foundation – Climate Justice, which aims to be 'a centre for thought leadership, education and advocacy on the struggle to secure global justice for those many victims of climate change who are usually forgotten – the poor, the disempowered and the marginalised across the world.'

Eimear Noone
(b. 1961)

Eimear Noone was born in Kilconnell, County Galway. A music graduate of Trinity College, Dublin, she has gone on to become a world renowned classical conductor and composer. Eimear was one of the first women to conduct at Dublin's National Concert Hall and the first to ever conduct at the Oscars! She has received numerous awards for her work in this male-dominated field and is now widely considered to be the world's premier conductor of video game music scores – a 21st-century music genre in its own right which she promotes with a passion with work on World of Warcraft, Zelda and Diablo. In the process, Eimear has proudly conducted some of the finest orchestras in the world including the Royal Philharmonic, the Philadelphia Orchestra, the Symphony Orchestra of Bretagne and the Sydney Symphony. She said, "I didn't really have an example to follow, but there's no physical reason why women shouldn't conduct."

Sonia O'Sullivan
(b. 1969)

Sonia O'Sullivan was born in Cobh, County Cork and went on to become Ireland's premier athlete and sportswoman throughout the '90s and '00s, dominating international distance running and winning numerous medals in the Olympic Games, World Championships and European Championships. Her world record, set in 1994, for 2000m remained unbroken for over 20 years and throughout the course of her career she racked up 8 gold, 6 silver and 2 bronze medals at the world's most important athletic competitions. She won a gold for the 5000m race in the 1995 World Championships in Gothenburg and a silver medal for the same distance in the 2000 Olympic Games in Sydney. She officially retired from the sport in 2007, although she still works as a commentator for RTÉ Sport during their coverage of high profile athletic events. Sonia has written two books; 'Running to Stand Still' published in 2001 and 'Sonia: My Story' in 2008. A statue to commemorate Sonia's remarkable achievements was erected in her home town in 2015.

Emma Dabiri

(b. undisclosed)

Emma Dabiri is the Dublin-born daughter of an Irish mother and a Nigerian father and although initially brought up in Atlanta, Georgia, she was just five years old when her family returned to Dublin. Finding herself to be the only black child in her school set her on an inquisitive path of learning what race and place have meant throughout history. After gaining a BA in African studies and history, Emma went on to become an author, social historian, model, writer, multi-media broadcaster and television presenter. She is a teaching fellow at SOAS University of London specialising in African studies and has researched a PhD on Visual Sociology titled 'Mixed-Race a Ghost Story'. Emma has chosen to fight race negativity with knowledge by dedicating her life to teaching, research and the publishing of her findings. Her debut book, Don't Touch My Hair was first published in 2019.

Sinéad Burke
(b. 1990)

Sinéad Burke, born and raised in Dublin, is an Irish writer, author, academic, fashion influencer, human rights activist and broadcaster. Sinéad was born with achondroplasia, a form of dwarfism which she didn't allow to hold her back in pursuing her early career as a primary school teacher and after graduating at the top of her class she received the Vere Foster Medal from Trinity College, Dublin. She became famous for her empowering TED talk 'Why Design Should Include Everyone', advocating that fashion and overall design needs to be more inclusive to those with disabilities. Sinéad was ranked on the BBC's list of the 100 most inspiring and influential women in the world for 2019 and she was appointed to the Council of State in Ireland to help amplify voices on issues of equality, access and education. As a co-founder of the Inclusive Fashion and Design Collective with Liz Jackson, Sinéad was invited to be a contributing editor of British Vogue as well as being the first 'little person' to ever grace its cover. She's also an ambassador for the Irish Society for the Prevention of Cruelty to Children and the Irish Girl Guides. Sinéad's popular podcast 'As Me' aims to challenge prejudices, deepen empathy and empower us to impact and change the world.

Be Creative!

Draw yourself in the role of your dreams here